Ric to the Rescue

written by Corinne Fenton

illustrated by Deborah Gross

raintree

Engage Literacy is published in 2013 by Raintree.
Raintree is an imprint of Capstone Global Library Limited, a company
incorporated in Engand and Wales having its registered office at 7 Pilgrim
Street, London, EC4V 6LB – Registered company number: 6695582
www.raintree.co.uk

Written by Corinne Fenton 2012
Lead authors Jay Dale and Anne Giulieri
Cover illustration and illustrations by Deborah Gross
Edited by Gwenda Smyth
UK edition edited by Dan Nunn, Catherine Veitch and Sian Smith
Designed by Susannah Low, Butterflyrocket Design

Rico to the Rescue
ISBN: 978 1 406 26506 4
10 9 8 7 6 5 4 3 2 1

Printed and bound in India.

Contents

Chapter 1
Five Fluffy Ducklings

Rico watched as five fluffy ducklings waddled behind their mother.

"Look at those ducklings," Rico said to Mum. "They're so tiny."

"Yes," answered Mum. "They're only a few days old."

The next day, when Rico went to check the ducklings, they were still there under their mother's wing.

But on the third day,
when Rico went to check,
he couldn't see any ducks at all!
Where were Mother Duck and her ducklings?

Cheep! Cheep! Cheep! Cheep!

Suddenly, Rico heard the soft cheeping
of the ducklings.
The sound was coming from under
the bushes.

Mum opened the pool gate
and Rico ran over to the bushes.
As he pushed some leaves away,
he saw five frightened ducklings
cuddled up together.

"I can't see their mother anywhere,"
Rico said to Mum.

So together they looked around the pool.
They looked under every bush
and in the flowers.
But they couldn't find
Mother Duck anywhere.

"Oh, dear!" said Mum.
"I think something must have happened
to Mother Duck."

Rico's eyes filled with tears.
"We've got to do something
to help the ducklings," he said.

Chapter 2
Catching Ducklings

While Mum rang the wildlife shelter,
Rico disappeared into the shed.
He came out with a cardboard box
and an old towel.

"That's just what we need," said Mum.
"The man at the wildlife shelter
said to put the ducklings in a box
and bring them to the shelter."

"Okay," said Rico, "but we need to catch
them first!"

13

14

Rico and Mum soon found out that catching
five little ducklings wasn't easy.
As soon as they reached for the ducklings,
the little birds ran away and jumped
into the pool.

"Well," smiled Rico,
"at least we know they can swim!"

At first, Rico and Mum tried to catch
the ducklings
from the side of the pool.
But when they got close, the ducklings
quickly swam off to the other side.

Suddenly, Rico had an idea!

Chapter 3
Rico Goes In

When Rico came out of the house,
he had his swimming costume on.
Mum laughed.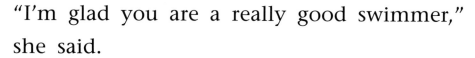
"I'm glad you are a really good swimmer,"
she said.

Rico smiled as he slid into the pool.
Then he quietly swam over to the ducklings.
He carefully caught them, one by one.
It was easy!
Soon, there were three ducklings in the box.

But the last two ducklings
were **not** so easy to catch.
Every time Rico swam close,
they would suddenly go under the water.

Rico tried and tried.
He was just about to give up,
when one of the ducklings
did a funny thing.
It started to swim towards him!
Rico reached out to grab it,
but the naughty little duckling
jumped out of the pool.
The other duckling followed.

Then the two little ducklings
ran off into the bushes.

Mum and Rico looked everywhere.
They could **hear** the ducklings cheeping,
but they couldn't **see** them.

Cheep! Cheep! Cheep! Cheep!

Then Rico had another idea.
"If we put the box near the bushes," he said,
"the three ducklings inside might cheep.
Then the other ducklings might come out
of the bushes looking for them."

"We could give it a try," answered Mum.

Rico put the box near the bushes.
It didn't take long before the ducklings
in the box began to cheep.

Cheep! Cheep! Cheep! Cheep!

Rico and Mum kept very still.
They watched as the two little ducklings
came out of the bushes
and waddled over to the box.

Rico and Mum crept slowly over to the box.
Then Mum carefully threw a towel
over the two ducklings.
Rico reached under the towel
and grabbed them.
"Gotcha!" he said.

Rico carefully placed the two ducklings in the box with their brothers and sisters.

"We did it!" said Rico.

"Yes," smiled Mum.
"Now, let's take these five fluffy ducklings to the wildlife shelter."